MATH TRAILBLAZERS™

Grade 2

Unit Resource Guide
Unit 13
Sampling, Sorting, and Science

SECOND EDITION

A Mathematical Journey Using Science and Language Arts

KENDALL/HUNT PUBLISHING COMPANY
4050 Westmark Drive   Dubuque, Iowa   52002

A TIMS® Curriculum
University of Illinois at Chicago

S0-ADY-804

UIC The University of Illinois
at Chicago

The original edition was based on work supported by the National Science Foundation under grant
No. MDR 9050226 and the University of Illinois at Chicago. Any opinions, findings, and conclusions
or recommendations expressed in this publication are those of the author(s) and do not necessarily
reflect the views of the granting agencies.

LETTER HOME

Sampling, Sorting, and Science

Date: _____

Dear Family Member:

In this unit, we will explore ways that scientists organize and analyze sets of data. For the purposes of our investigation, we have collected a large assortment of container lids. Your child will use these lids to sort a smaller sample in two ways, to display the data in a table, and to graph the information.

Your child will also read about the adventures of Professor Robinson and his daughter Betty, who camp in the Amazon rain forest to study monkeys. Ask your child to tell you about how they investigated the types of foods the monkeys eat.

You can reinforce our classroom experiences at home:

- **Investigating Food Containers.** Ask your child to predict which type of food container—paper, plastic, or metal—is most common in your home. Then, ask your child to describe the steps he or she would take to check this prediction. (For this activity it is not necessary to actually do the collecting and sorting.)

- **Math Facts.** Continue to help your child learn the subtraction facts by practicing with the *Triangle Flash Cards: Group C*. These cards will be sent home for homework.

Thank you for your continued efforts to bring math awareness into your child's world.

Sincerely,

_____

Students draw pictures showing how they sorted the lids.

UNIT 13 · UNIT OUTLINE

Sampling, Sorting, and Science

Pacing Suggestions

The activities in this unit develop mathematics concepts using science process skills. Utilize *Math Trailblazers™* connections to other subjects:

- Read and discuss the *Adventure Book* story in Lesson 2 *Monkey Business* during language arts or science.
- Lesson 4 *Undercover Investigation* is a laboratory investigation. Collect and organize the data during science time.

Components Key: SG = Student Guide, AB = Adventure Book, URG = Unit Resource Guide, and DPP = Daily Practice and Problems

	Sessions	Description	Supplies
LESSON 1 **Classifying and Sorting Lids** SG pages 344–350 URG pages 14–20 DPP A–D	2	**ACTIVITY:** Students sort a sample of container lids by one variable, then organize, graph, and analyze the data.	• class collection of container lids • plastic bags • envelopes
LESSON 2 **Monkey Business** AB pages 65–76 URG pages 21–26 DPP E–F	1	**ADVENTURE BOOK:** The class reads about Professor Robinson and his daughter Betty as they find out what types of food monkeys eat in an Amazon rain forest.	
LESSON 3 **Two-Variable Sorting** SG pages 351–356 URG pages 27–33 DPP G–J	2	**ACTIVITY:** Student pairs sort a sample of lids by two variables and their corresponding values, make data tables, and analyze the data. **ASSESSMENT PAGES:** *Frank and Kaley's Lids,* Student Guide, pages 355–356.	• class collection of container lids • plastic bags

	Sessions	Description	Supplies
LESSON 4 **Undercover Investigation** SG pages 357–362 URG pages 34–41 DPP K–P	3	**LAB:** Student pairs sort a sample of lids by two variables, organize the data in tables and graphs, analyze the data, and compare the class results to their own. **ASSESSMENT PAGES:** *Mena Sorts for Recycling,* Student Guide, pages 361–362.	• class collection of container lids

CONNECTIONS

A current list of connections is available at www.mathtrailblazers.com.

Literature

Suggested Titles

■ Goodall, Jane. *The Chimpanzee Family Book.* Photographs by Michael Neugebauer. North-South Books, New York, 1997.

■ Goodall, Jane. *The Chimpanzees I Love: Saving Their World and Ours.* Scholastic Press, New York, 2001.

Software

■ *Graphers* is a data-graphing tool appropriate for young students.

■ *Kid Pix* helps students draw, write, and illustrate math concepts.

■ *Math Concepts One . . . Two . . . Three!* provides practice sorting different attributes and identifying patterns.

■ *Mighty Math Carnival Countdown* provides practice sorting sets of numbers by various attributes including size, more/less, and even/odd.

■ *Sunbuddy Math Playhouse* sorts musical instruments by an increasing number of attributes.

■ *Thinkin' Things Collection 1* observes a row of birds with various attributes and builds the next bird in line. Students look for various attributes of the characters.

BACKGROUND

Sampling, Sorting, and Science

In this unit, students explore ways that scientists use samples and surveys to answer questions. The students will use a collection of assorted container lids to practice sampling and sorting techniques. Lesson 1 *Classifying and Sorting Lids* reviews sorting a sample by one variable (attribute), such as color. Each group of children takes a sample of the class collection, sorts and organizes the items in their sample, and then makes inferences from the data they have collected. In Lesson 3 *Two-Variable Sorting,* children explore different ways of organizing data when they study two variables at once. In Lesson 4 *Undercover Investigation,* the class uses the TIMS Laboratory Method to collaborate on one question about the class collection of lids. Students conduct the investigation and make a prediction about the total population of lids. A final analysis of the class data as well as a comparison with that of partners' data leads children to an understanding that a study is usually more valid when numerous samples are considered.

Students also read the *Monkey Business* Adventure Book. In this story, set in a South American rain forest, students see why scientists might be interested in studying more than one variable.

Discussion questions help children understand the significance of using each step of the TIMS Laboratory Method as well as what can be inferred about a population by examining smaller samples.

Variables and Values

A **variable** is something that changes or varies in an investigation. **Values** are possible outcomes for the variables. You may use the terms *variable* and *values* together with terms more familiar to students such as *attribute* and *categories*. In the *Student Guide* we use the terms *variable* and *groups for sorting.* For example, the items in a set of lids may vary in color, shape, diameter, thickness, texture, material, and mass. Each of these variables may be further distinguished by considering its values. For instance, the values of the variable *shape* may be circular, square, rectangular, or oval. That is, if we choose to sort the lids using the variable *shape,* our groups for sorting can be labeled circular, square, rectangular, and oval. It is important that children have a clear understanding of the terms you use and that students can use vocabulary that makes sense to them to express their ideas.

Assessment Indicators

- Can students sort and classify objects?
- Can students represent the elements of a laboratory investigation in a drawing?
- Can students collect and organize data in a table?
- Can students make and interpret bar graphs?
- Can students sort and classify a group of objects using two variables?
- Can students use data to make predictions and solve problems?
- Do students demonstrate fluency with the related subtraction facts for Group C?

OBSERVATIONAL ASSESSMENT RECORD

(A1) Can students sort and classify objects?

(A2) Can students represent the elements of a laboratory investigation in a drawing?

(A3) Can students collect and organize data in a table?

(A4) Can students make and interpret bar graphs?

(A5) Can students sort and classify a group of objects using two variables?

(A6) Can students use data to make predictions and solve problems?

(A7) Do students demonstrate fluency with the related subtraction facts for Group C?

(A8) _____

Name	A1	A2	A3	A4	A5	A6	A7	A8	Comments
1.									
2.									
3.									
4.									
5.									
6.									
7.									
8.									
9.									
10.									
11.									
12.									
13.									

Name	A1	A2	A3	A4	A5	A6	A7	A8	Comments
14.									
15.									
16.									
17.									
18.									
19.									
20.									
21.									
22.									
23.									
24.									
25.									
26.									
27.									
28.									
29.									
30.									
31.									
32.									

Daily Practice and Problems

Sampling, Sorting, and Science

Two Daily Practice and Problems (DPP) items are included for each class session listed in the Unit Outline. A Scope and Sequence Chart for the DPP can be found in the *Teacher Implementation Guide.*

A DPP Menu for Unit 13

Icons in the Teacher Notes column designate the subject matter of the DPP items. Each item falls into one or more of the categories listed below. A menu of the DPP items for Unit 13 follows.

N Number Sense	**Computation**	**Time**	**Geometry**
H, J, K, M	B, D, E, H–K, M, P	L	
Math Facts	**$ Money**	**Measurement**	**Data**
A, C, F, G, K, N, O	E, G	P	

Practice and Assessment of the Subtraction Facts

DPP items in this unit provide review and assessment of the subtraction facts related to the facts in Group C (6 − 3, 7 − 3, 7 − 4, 8 − 4, 9 − 4, 9 − 5, 10 − 5, 11 − 5, 11 − 6, 12 − 5, 12 − 7, 12 − 6). Facts in this group can be solved by using doubles to find half doubles, making a ten, using a ten, and by reasoning from known facts. DPP item A asks students to use the *Triangle Flash Cards* to study these facts. *Triangle Flash Cards: Group C Subtraction Facts* can be found in the *Student*

Guide as homework for Lesson 1. See DPP items C, F, G, K, and N for practice with these facts and item O for an assessment. Use Assessment Indicator (A7) and the *Observational Assessment Record* to document students' progress with these facts.

For information on the practice and assessment of the addition and subtraction facts in Grade 2, see the DPP Guides for Units 3 and 11 and the *Grade 2 Facts Resource Guide.* For a detailed explanation of our approach to learning and assessing the facts in Grades K–5, see the TIMS Tutor: *Math Facts* in the *Teacher Implementation Guide.*

Daily Practice and Problems

Students may solve the items individually, in groups, or as a class. The items may also be assigned for homework.

Student Questions	Teacher Notes

 Triangle Flash Cards: Group C Subtraction Facts

With a partner, use your *Triangle Flash Cards* to practice subtraction facts. One partner covers the corner with a number in the circle. This number is the answer to a subtraction fact. Use the other two numbers to solve a subtraction fact. Separate the cards into three piles: those facts you know and can answer quickly, those facts that you can figure out with a strategy, and those that you need to learn. Make a list of the facts in the last two piles.

Put the cards back into one pile and go through them again. This time, your partner covers the number in the square. This number will now be the answer. Use the other two numbers to solve a subtraction fact. Separate the cards into three piles again. Add the facts in the last two piles to your list. Take the list home to practice.

Repeat the directions for your partner.

Discuss the strategies that you use.

Triangle Flash Cards: Group C Subtraction Facts are located in the *Student Guide* and the *Unit Resource Guide* Generic Section.

Remind students to take their cards home to study for homework. Give students envelopes to store their cards.

Inform students when the quiz on the facts in Group C will be given. This quiz appears in DPP item O.

Peanut Treats

Bob, the monkey trainer, is giving six monkeys a treat. In each of the six cups, Bob wants to place four peanuts. How many peanuts does Bob need?

Demonstrate the problem with counters and cups. Ask students to write a number sentence to describe the problem.

$4 + 4 + 4 + 4 + 4 + 4 =$
24 peanuts or $4 \times 6 = 24$ peanuts are two possible number sentences.

 Subtraction Facts

A. $8 - 4 =$ B. $11 - 5 =$

C. $9 - 5 =$ D. $12 - 7 =$

E. $6 - 3 =$ F. $7 - 3 =$

G. $12 - 6 =$ H. $9 - 4 =$

Explain your strategy for E.

A. 4	B. 6
C. 4	D. 5
E. 3	F. 4
G. 6	H. 5

One possible strategy: 6 is double 3 so 3 is a half double. $3 + 3 = 6$.

Field Trip

The second graders took a field trip to the zoo. One school bus carried 48 people. The other school bus carried 46 people. How many people went on the field trip?

Encourage students to share their strategies for solving the addition problem. Students may use mental math, paper and pencil, or the *200 Chart*, to name a few.

94 people.

 At the Zoo

Helen bought a hot dog and a cola for $1.37 at the zoo. She gave the vendor $2.00.

1. How much change should she get back?

2. What coins could she get back?

1. 63¢

2. Answers will vary. She could get 6 dimes and 3 pennies or 2 quarters, 2 nickels, and 3 pennies.

Student Questions	Teacher Notes

F **Subtraction Story**

Write a story and draw a picture to show 12 − 5. Write the number sentence.

Name three other number sentences that are in the same fact family.

Stories and pictures will vary.

12 − 5 = 7

12 − 7 = 5

5 + 7 = 12

7 + 5 = 12

G **Earning Money**

1. Cathy earned 10 quarters shoveling snow. Her sister Anne earned 5 quarters. How many more quarters did Cathy earn than Anne?

2. How much money did Cathy earn?

3. How much money did Anne earn?

4. How much more money did Cathy earn than Anne?

1. 5 quarters
2. $2.50
3. $1.25
4. $1.25

H **Number Sense**

72 + 25

1. Is the answer less than 50?

2. Is the answer between 50 and 100?

3. Is the answer more than 100?

4. Is the answer closer to 75 or 100?

75 + 25 = 100. 72 is just a little less than 75 so 72 + 25 is just a little less than 100.

1. no
2. yes
3. no
4. closer to 100.

Student Questions	Teacher Notes

 Sharing Peanuts

Elaine has 28 peanuts. She wants to give them to four of her friends. How many peanuts will each friend get if she shares them equally?

7 peanuts

Encourage students to use counters or draw pictures to help them solve the problem.

 More Than One Way

A. 56 + 77 =

B. 94 − 37 =

C. 60 − 45 =

Ask students to solve each problem two different ways.

A. 133

B. 57

C. 15

K Subtraction with Tens and Hundreds

1. 7 − 4 = _____

2. 70 − 40 = _____

3. 700 − 400 = _____

4. _____ = 11 − 6

5. _____ = 110 − 60

6. _____ = 1100 − 600

1. 3

2. 30

3. 300

4. 5

5. 50

6. 500

Student Questions	Teacher Notes

L Time

It is 4:30.

1. Franco came home from band practice a half hour ago. What time did he come home?

2. In one hour he will set the dinner table. At what time will he set the table?

3. In four hours he will go to bed. At what time will Franco go to bed?

1. 4:00
2. 5:30
3. 8:30

M Number Sense

$87 + 29$

1. Is the answer less than 50?

2. Is the answer between 50 and 100?

3. Is the answer more than 100?

4. Is the answer closer to 100 or 125?

$75 + 25 = 100$. 87 and 29 are both larger than 75 and 25, by 12 and 4. So the answer is more than 100 and closer to 125.

1. no
2. no
3. yes
4. 125

N Word Problems

A. Sol made 11 valentines and gave 6 to his friends. He gave the rest of the cards to his cousins. How many valentines did Sol give to his cousins?

B. Tess had 12 candy hearts. Sandy had 5 fewer hearts than Tess. How many candy hearts did Sandy have?

A. 5 cards

B. 7 hearts

Have students explain their strategies.

Student Questions	Teacher Notes

O **Subtraction Facts Quiz: Group C**

A. $6 - 3 =$ _____

B. $9 - 5 =$ _____

C. $11 - 6 =$ _____

D. _____ $= 7 - 3$

E. $8 - 4 =$ _____

F. _____ $= 12 - 7$

G. $11 - 5 =$ _____

H. $9 - 4 =$ _____

I. $12 - 6 =$ _____

J. $7 - 4 =$ _____

K. _____ $= 10 - 5$

L. $12 - 5 =$ _____

Explain how you solved D.

A. 3
B. 4
C. 5
D. 4
E. 4
F. 5
G. 6
H. 5
I. 6
J. 3
K. 5
L. 7

Answers will vary. One possible response: 7 is 1 more than the double of 3; 1 more than 3 is 4.

 Rocks

1. Marjorie measured the volume of a rock. She filled a graduated cylinder to 40 cc. After she placed the rock inside, the water rose to 48 cc. What is the volume of her rock?

2. If Marjorie's rock had a twin and she placed it inside the cylinder too, to what level would the water rise?

1. 8 cc
2. 56 cc

Daily Practice and Problems

A. *Triangle Flash Cards:*
   Group C Subtraction Facts (URG p. 8)

With a partner, use your *Triangle Flash Cards* to practice subtraction facts. One partner covers the corner with a number in the circle. This number is the answer to a subtraction fact. Use the other two numbers to solve a subtraction fact. Separate the cards into three piles: those facts you know and can answer quickly, those facts that you can figure out with a strategy, and those that you need to learn. Make a list of the facts in the last two piles.

Put the cards back into one pile and go through them again. This time, your partner covers the number in the square. This number will now be the answer. Use the other two numbers to solve a subtraction fact. Separate the cards into three piles again. Add the facts in the last two piles to your list. Take the list home to practice.

Repeat the directions for your partner.

Discuss the strategies that you use.

B. Peanut Treats (URG p. 9)

Bob, the monkey trainer, is giving six monkeys a treat. In each of the six cups, Bob wants to place four peanuts. How many peanuts does Bob need?

C. Subtraction Facts (URG p. 9)

A. $8 - 4 =$	B. $11 - 5 =$
C. $9 - 5 =$	D. $12 - 7 =$
E. $6 - 3 =$	F. $7 - 3 =$
G. $12 - 6 =$	H. $9 - 4 =$

Explain your strategy for E.

D. Field Trip (URG p. 9)

The second graders took a field trip to the zoo. One school bus carried 48 people. The other school bus carried 46 people. How many people went on the field trip?

Suggestions for using the DPPs are on pages 18–19.

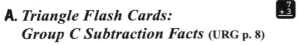

LESSON GUIDE 1

Classifying and Sorting Lids

Estimated Class Sessions: **2**

Students discuss different ways of classifying lids. Each group chooses a variable, sorts the lids into groups according to the values of that variable, and counts the number of each type of lid. The data is entered into a data table and graph.

Key Content

- Identifying variables for a collection of objects.
- Identifying values of variables (groups for sorting).
- Sorting and classifying objects into categories.
- Representing the elements of a laboratory investigation in a drawing.
- Collecting, organizing, graphing, and analyzing data.
- Making predictions based on samples.
- Solving problems involving addition and subtraction.

Key Vocabulary

sample
value
variable

Materials List

Print Materials for Students

	Math Facts and Daily Practice and Problems	Activity	Homework	Written Assessment
Student Book — Student Guide		*Classifying and Sorting Lids* Page 344 and *Lids Data Table* Page 345	*Recycling Lids* Pages 347–348 and *Triangle Flash Cards: Group C Subtraction Facts* Pages 349–350	
Teacher Resources — Facts Resource Guide	DPP Items 13A & 13C Use the *Triangle Flash Cards: Group C Subtraction Facts* to practice the subtraction facts for this group.			
Unit Resource Guide	DPP Items A–D Pages 8–9			DPP Item D *Field Trip* Page 9
Generic Section		*Vertical Bar Graph,* 1 per student		

○ *available on Teacher Resource CD*

All Transparency Masters, Blackline Masters, and Assessment Blackline Masters in the Unit Resource Guide are on the Teacher Resource CD.

Supplies for Each Student Group

about 30 lids
clear plastic bag
envelopes for storing flash cards

Materials for the Teacher

Observational Assessment Record (Unit Resource Guide, Pages 5–6 and Teacher Resource CD)

Content Note

A **variable** is something that changes or *varies*.
Values are possible outcomes of the variables. If a scientist is studying the heights of second graders, the variable under investigation is height, since it varies from child to child. Possible values of the variable (height) are 45 inches, 40 inches, and 43 inches. In the investigations in this unit, students choose the variables they want to study. For example, they can choose to sort the lids by color, material, shape, or mass. Possible values for the variable color are red, green, or blue and possible values for the variable shape are square, circular, or oval.

Students use variables in laboratory investigations throughout *Math Trailblazers*. At this point in the curriculum, the focus should be on these ideas—not on the vocabulary. As you discuss students' investigations, use appropriate terms while varying the language so that students understand the concepts. For example, in discussion with children ask:

- *How many different ways can we sort the lids? What variables or attributes can we study?* (color, shape, size, material)
- *If we choose to study the variable color, what values can we use to sort them? In other words, what are the names of the groups that you will use to sort the lids?* (red, green, clear, blue, white)

Encourage students to use vocabulary that is both appropriate and comfortable for them, so that they can express their ideas easily. Students will be expected to use more formal vocabulary in later grades.

TIMS Tip

In order to obtain data that will provide good distributions in a bar graph, you may want to limit the number of values students study to two or three.

Before the Activity

Encourage each student to bring in at least ten clean lids for your class collection. Try to collect enough lids of various sizes, shapes, and colors so that each group of four students will have approximately fifty lids. Group lids into bags of about fifty.

Developing the Activity

Show the class all the lids in the class collection. Explain that each group will work with a **sample,** or some of the lids in the collection. Let students brainstorm questions they might have about the lids. Record students' questions on the blackboard. Some possible questions follow:

- *What materials are lids made of?*
- *What are the sizes of lids?*
- *What colors do lids come in?*
- *What is the weight of most lids?*
- *Is there one shape that is most common for lids?*
- *Is there a particular thickness that is most common?*
- *Do most lids have a smooth surface?*
- *Are screw-on lids more common than snap-on lids?*

Ask the class what variable they need to consider in order to answer each question. List the variables that students suggest, such as material, size, color, weight or mass, shape, thickness, and texture. Then, select one variable to discuss, such as material. Ask students to identify the values of that variable using questions similar to the following:

- *If we are interested in the material (color, shape, or size) of the lids, name ways that you can sort the lids into groups.*
- *What will be the names of the groups that you sort the lids into? The names of the groups are values of that variable.*

For example, one class decided that the values of material they would study were: plastic, metal, and metal with rubber inside. As in Unit 3 *Buttons,* students may have to come up with their own definitions for values of some variables.

Some possible variables and values follow.

- Material: plastic, metal, and metal with rubber inside
- Color: red, white, clear, black, green, yellow, silver, gold, and blue
- Mass or weight: light, medium, and heavy when compared with standard masses on a pan balance

- Size: small, medium, large, and very large when compared with standard sizes, such as small, medium, large, and very large circles or squares drawn on a sheet of paper
- Shape: circular, rectangular, square, oval, triangular
- Thickness: thin (less than 1 cm), medium (1–2 cm), and thick (2 or more cm)
- Texture: smooth or bumpy
- Kind of top: screw-on or snap-on

Divide the class into groups of four. Give each group a bag of lids. Ask them to examine their sample, agree on something to study about the lids, and write it at the top of the *Classifying and Sorting Lids* Activity Page. Ask students to identify the variable and the groups into which they will sort the lids. Have students draw a picture that shows how they will sort the lids. In particular, the variable and its values (the names of the groups) should be shown in the picture. See Figure 1 for a sample drawing.

Figure 1: *A picture communicating the variable and values in the lab*

Some students may find it necessary to define their groups in detail. For example, if students decide to sort the lids by color, they may need to decide what the main color is on lids that have text or designs on them. Stress the importance of students agreeing on their definitions before they begin to sort the lids.

After students have illustrated how they will sort the lids, they should sort the lids and record the data in the table on the *Lids Data Table* Activity Page. Have them fill in the title of the left column with the variable they are studying and write the names of their groups below it. See Figure 2. Finally, ask them to graph their data using a blank *Vertical Bar Graph.*

Lids

C Color	N Number
gold	10
black	5
white	10
silver	9

Figure 2: *A student data table*

***Student Guide* - Page 344**

***Student Guide* - Page 345**

Name _____ **Date** _____

Recycling Lids

Homework

> Dear Family Member:
>
> Your child sorted the lids we collected by color, shape, size, or the type of material each was made of. Discuss the data table below with your child.
>
> Thank you for your cooperation.

Tina and James collected lids from their homes. Then they sorted them by material and put their data in a table.

Lid Material

M Material	N Number
metal only	35
metal with rubber inside	10
plastic	51
paper	3

Show how you solved each problem.

1. What was the least common type of lid material?

   _____

2. How many more plastic lids than paper lids were there?

   _____

Student Guide - Page 347

Name _____ **Date** _____

3. How many more plastic lids than lids with metal were there?

   _____

   _____

4. How many lids did Tina and James collect?

   _____

   _____

5. Were more than half of the lids made of plastic? Explain.

   _____

   _____

   _____

Student Guide - Page 348

Ask students to reread the statement they wrote on the first activity page. Have them analyze the data in the table and in the graph, and draw a conclusion from their investigations. Ask each group to summarize, based on their data, what they learned about the lids. Guide them by asking questions like those below. Note that the questions use the term *groups* to develop the concept of values of variables. For example, you can ask, *"How many groups did you sort your lids into?"* Or, you can ask, *"How many values for your variable did you find?"*

- *What are the names of your groups?*
- *Did you have trouble deciding on which group to put a lid in? Did you run into any problems sorting your lids?*
- *Were your lids evenly divided among the groups or not?*
- *Which kind of lid did you have the most of?*
- *Which kind of lid did you have the least of?*
- *Predict the most common color (shape, size, or material) of lid in the whole class collection.*

In the concluding lab activity in this unit, we will discuss the question of whether a sample can be relied upon to give accurate information about the whole collection.

Suggestions for Teaching the Lesson

Math Facts

DPP item A reminds students to practice with the *Triangle Flash Cards: Group C Subtraction Facts.* Item C provides more subtraction facts practice.

Homework and Practice

- *The Recycling Lids* Homework Pages provide students with practice using data to solve computation problems.
- DPP items B and D are both word problems that build computational skills. Item B involves multiplication and item D involves two-digit addition.
- Assign the *Triangle Flash Cards: Group C Subtraction Facts* in the *Student Guide* as ongoing homework. Discuss possible strategies for learning the subtraction facts for this group including using doubles, half doubles, and near doubles.

Assessment

- Did students choose a variable that made sense? Did they define the values of the variable appropriately? Could they sort lids according to the values of the variable and fill in the *Lids Data Table* clearly? Could students make a bar graph independently? In particular, were they able to number the vertical axis and label both axes correctly? Were their answers to the Explore question related to their data? Record your observations on the *Observational Assessment Record*.

- Use DPP item D to assess students' abilities to add two-digit numbers.

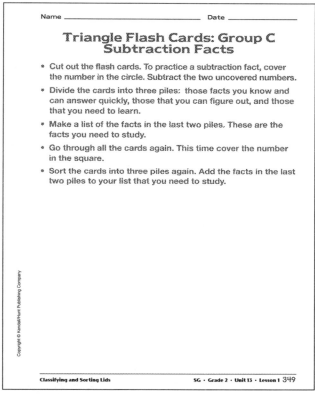

Student Guide - Page 349

Student Guide - Page 350

AT A GLANCE

Math Facts and Daily Practice and Problems (A7)

DPP item A provides practice with the subtraction facts using *Triangle Flash Cards*. Item C provides further subtraction facts practice. Items B and D are word problems that use computation skills.

Developing the Activity (A1) (A2) (A3) (A4)

1. Students brainstorm questions they have about the types of lids.
2. Students list the variables that could be considered about lids.
3. Students identify values of variables.
4. Student groups choose a variable to study using a sample of the class collection of lids.
5. Students complete the *Classifying and Sorting Lids* and the *Lids Data Table* Activity Pages in the *Student Guide* using the data from their sample.
6. Students graph their data on a *Vertical Bar Graph* from the Generic Section.
7. Students analyze their data and draw conclusions.

Homework

1. Assign the *Recycling Lids* Homework Pages.
2. Send home the *Triangle Flash Cards: Group C Subtraction Facts* so students can study these subtraction facts with a family member.

Assessment

1. Use Assessment Indicators (A1, A3, A4) and the *Observational Assessment Record* to note students' abilities to sort and classify objects and to collect, organize, graph, and analyze data.
2. Use DPP item D to assess students' progress adding two-digit numbers.

Notes:

Answer Key • Lesson 1: Classifying and Sorting Lids

Student Guide

Classifying and Sorting Lids (SG p. 344)

*Answers will vary. Students might want to find out: the materials the lids are made of, the sizes of the lids, colors of the lids, weight of the lids, etc.

*See Figure 1 in Lesson Guide 1 for a sample picture.

Lids Data Table (SG p. 345)

*See Figure 2 in Lesson Guide 1 for a sample data table.

Bar graphs will vary depending on data collected.

Descriptions will vary.

Recycling Lids (SG pp. 347–348)

Questions 1–5

1. paper
2. 48 more plastic lids
3. 6 more plastic lids
4. 99 lids
5. Yes; Solution strategies will vary. One possible strategy is to estimate half of 99. 50 is a good estimate. Compare the estimate to the number of plastic lids: 51 > 50.

*Answers and/or discussion are included in the Lesson Guide.

LESSON GUIDE 2
Monkey Business

Estimated Class Sessions: 1

Professor Robinson and his daughter Betty are camping in the Amazon rain forest. They study three types of monkeys: howler, squirrel, and spider. Betty wants to know what types of food the monkeys eat. Before starting out, the Robinsons decide how they will organize the data they gather. After they conduct their investigation, Betty tallies the types of foods each troop eats and organizes the data in three bar graphs. She learns that most of the howler monkeys eat leaves but some eat fruits; the squirrel monkeys eat fruits, flowers, and insects; and half of the spider monkeys eat fruits while the other half eat nuts. Both Professor Robinson and Betty agree that they need more data to be sure their results are valid.

Key Content

- Sampling a population.
- Collecting and organizing data.
- Making predictions based on a sample.
- Connecting mathematics and science to language arts: reading about a scientific field study.

Daily Practice and Problems

E. At the Zoo (URG p. 9)

Helen bought a hot dog and a cola for $1.37 at the zoo. She gave the vendor $2.00.

1. How much change should she get back?

2. What coins could she get back?

F. Subtraction Story (URG p. 10)

Write a story and draw a picture to show 12 − 5. Write the number sentence.

Name three other number sentences that are in the same fact family.

Suggestions for using the DPPs are on page 26.

Key Vocabulary

territory
troop

Materials List

Print Materials for Students

		Math Facts and Daily Practice and Problems	Activity
Student Book	Adventure Book		*Monkey Business* Pages 65–76
Teacher Resources	Facts Resource Guide	DPP Item 13F	
	Unit Resource Guide	DPP Items E–F Pages 9–10	

available on Teacher Resource CD

All Transparency Masters, Blackline Masters, and Assessment Blackline Masters in the Unit Resource Guide are on the Teacher Resource CD.

Adventure Book - Page 65

Page 65

- *The title of this story is* Monkey Business. *What do you think the story will be about?*

Adventure Book - Page 66

Page 66

- *Where is South America? Locate South America on a map.*
- *What is a rain forest?*

It is a forest in which more than 100 inches of rain falls each year.

Discussion Prompts

Page 68

- *Can you think of anything else monkeys might eat?*
- *Why is it important for scientists to find out what monkeys eat in the rain forests?*

Scientists find out if certain nuts, fruits, and other foods can be harvested without taking needed food away from the monkeys.

- *What is a "troop" of monkeys?*

A group of monkeys.

Adventure Book - Page 68

Page 69

- *Why is it important to get organized first?*

To decrease the number of errors in the data collection process.

- *What variables are they studying?*

They are studying two variables in this experiment—types of monkeys and the food they eat.

- *What types of monkeys are they studying?*

Three values of monkeys—howler, squirrel, and spider.

- *What types of food are they studying?*

Five values of food—fruits, flowers, leaves, nuts, and insects.

Adventure Book - Page 69

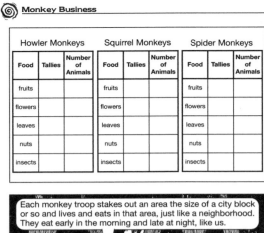

Adventure Book - Page 70

Adventure Book - Page 71

Discussion Prompts

Page 70

- *Why do they need three data tables instead of just one?*

Because they are studying more than one variable, it is difficult to organize the data in just one table. This way they can easily record the different types of food for each monkey.

- *What happens if Betty finds another food that the monkeys eat?*

She can add the food to the data table.

Page 71

- *Why is it important not to scare the monkeys?*

They might act differently and not eat. They might run away to a safer place.

Discussion Prompts

Page 74

- *Why do you think the spider monkeys are called "gymnasts of the jungle"?*

They swing through the trees like a gymnast swings on parallel bars.

Adventure Book - Page 74

Page 75

- *Did Professor Robinson and Betty see more spider monkeys or squirrel monkeys? Is it easy to tell?*

They saw more squirrel monkeys, but it's not easy to see. The data in each graph has to be totaled.

- *Did they see more howler monkeys than squirrel monkeys?*

No, they saw one less howler monkey than squirrel monkeys.

- *Compare the food that the howlers eat to the food squirrel monkeys eat.*

The howlers mostly eat leaves, but some like to eat fruits. The squirrel monkeys mostly eat fruits and flowers, but some like to eat insects.

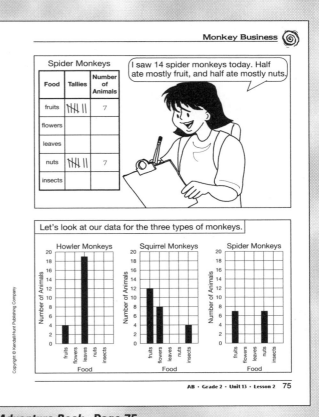

Adventure Book - Page 75

Adventure Book - Page 76

Discussion Prompts

Page 76

- *Why do the Robinsons need more data?*

The more data they get, the more certain they can be that their conclusions are correct. They have to be careful other variables do not affect their results.

- *What are some other variables that might affect their results?*

Some possible examples are the time of day, the time of year, or the weather.

- *What are some reasons that these variables might affect our results?*

Different types of food might be available at different times or in different weather. Monkeys might need different kinds of nutrition at different times. We really don't know the answers to these questions until we study them. But we have to think about what other variables might affect our results to make sure they are valid.

- *What do you think "defining their territory" means?*

The howlers are telling the other monkeys where they are.

Suggestions for Teaching the Lesson

Math Facts

DPP item F uses fact families, drawings, and story writing to provide practice with addition and subtraction facts.

Homework and Practice

- DPP item E contains word problems that require computation with money.
- Remind students to practice the subtraction facts for Group C using their *Triangle Flash Cards*.

Literature Connection

- Goodall, Jane. *The Chimpanzee Family Book.* Photographs by Michael Neugebauer. North-South Books, New York, 1997.
- Goodall, Jane. *The Chimpanzees I Love: Saving Their World and Ours.* Scholastic Press, New York, 2001.

LESSON GUIDE

Two-Variable Sorting

Estimated Class Sessions: 2

Two-Variable Sorting builds on the preceding lesson by exploring ways to organize data when studying two variables. For example, students might decide to find out whether plastic lids are the same size as metal lids. In that case, children look at two variables—materials and size. A brainstorming session encourages students to think of ways to organize the two-variable data in one or more tables. The class then collaborates on developing the tables and analyzing the results.

Key Content

- Sorting a collection of objects by two variables.
- Collecting and organizing data when two variables are studied.

Daily Practice and Problems

G. Earning Money (URG p. 10)

1. Cathy earned 10 quarters shoveling snow. Her sister Anne earned 5 quarters. How many more quarters did Cathy earn than Anne?

2. How much money did Cathy earn?

3. How much money did Anne earn?

4. How much more money did Cathy earn than Anne?

H. Number Sense (URG p. 10)

$72 + 25$

1. Is the answer less than 50?

2. Is the answer between 50 and 100?

3. Is the answer more than 100?

4. Is the answer closer to 75 or 100?

I. Sharing Peanuts (URG p. 11)

Elaine has 28 peanuts. She wants to give them to four of her friends. How many peanuts will each friend get if she shares them equally?

J. More Than One Way (URG p. 11)

A. $56 + 77 =$

B. $94 - 37 =$

C. $60 - 45 =$

Suggestions for using the DPPs are on page 31.

Materials List

Print Materials for Students

		Math Facts and Daily Practice and Problems	Activity	Homework	Written Assessment
Student Book	**Student Guide**		*Two-Variable Sorting* Pages 351–352	*Keenya and Michael's Lids* Pages 353–354	*Frank and Kaley's Lids* Pages 355–356
Teacher Resources	**Facts Resource Guide**	DPP Item 13G			
	Unit Resource Guide	DPP Items G–J Pages 10–11			

available on Teacher Resource CD

All Transparency Masters, Blackline Masters, and Assessment Blackline Masters in the Unit Resource Guide are on the Teacher Resource CD.

Supplies for Each Student Pair

20–30 lids
plastic bag

Materials for the Teacher

Observational Assessment Record (Unit Resource Guide, Pages 5–6 and Teacher Resource CD)

Before the Activity

Place about 20–30 lids in a plastic bag for each student pair.

Developing the Activity

Tell students that they will explore how to study two variables at once. Remind them that Professor Robinson and his daughter Betty studied two variables in the *Monkey Business* Adventure Book.

Discuss possible purposes for studying two variables with the lids, such as whether different size lids are a particular color. Encourage students to think of things they could study about the lids. Format the requests as questions. Make a list of students' questions. Some possible questions involving two variables follow:

- Material and size: *Are metal lids the same size as plastic lids?*

- Size and color: *Are large lids the same colors as small lids?*

- Material and shape: *Do metal and plastic lids come in the same shapes?*

- Thickness and color: *Is the thickness of lids related to their color?*

- Material and texture: *Is there a difference in the texture of plastic lids and metal lids?*

- Kind of top and material: *Is a screw-on or snap-on lid more commonly made of metal than of plastic?*

We suggest that the class agree on one question to study. Encourage student pairs to work as independently as possible to come up with different methods of organizing their data. Students may realize that there are many different ways to organize data. In the lab in Lesson 4, students will work in a more structured setting.

Remind students before they begin their investigation, that they must decide how to organize the data they will collect. You might suggest that students sort their lids first, then decide on the data tables they want to make. The process of grouping and sorting the lids might suggest ways of organizing and recording the data.

Distribute a bag of about 20–30 lids to each student pair. Each student writes the purpose of the investigation and draws a picture that shows the two

Name _____ Date _____

Two-Variable Sorting

Using your sample of lids, what do you want to find out?

Purpose: I want to find out _____

Draw a picture. Show how you will sort the lids two ways. Show the two variables and the groups for sorting each variable. Write the names of the variables and the names of the groups.

Two-Variable Sorting   SG · Grade 2 · Unit 13 · Lesson 3   351

Student Guide - Page 351

Name _____ Date _____

Work with your partner to decide how to organize your data for sorting two variables. Draw your data tables and fill them in.

352 SG · Grade 2 · Unit 13 · Lesson 3   Two-Variable Sorting

Student Guide - Page 352

Student Guide - Page 353

Name _____ **Date** _____

Keenya and Michael's Lids

Homework

Keenya and Michael chose to find out if metal lids were the same size as plastic lids.

They sorted their lids and made the two data tables on the next page.

Use the tables on the following page to answer the questions.

1. Are there more small, medium, or large lids? _____
2. What is the most common size of plastic lids? _____

Two-Variable Sorting   SG · Grade 2 · Unit 13 · Lesson 3 353

Student Guide - Page 354

Name _____ **Date** _____

Metal Lids			Plastic Lids	

S Size	N Number
small	7
medium	5
large	29

S Size	N Number
small	3
medium	30
large	8

3. What is the most common size of metal lids? _____
4. Are there more metal lids or plastic lids? _____
5. How could you organize Keenya and Michael's data another way? Draw your tables below.

354 SG · Grade 2 · Unit 13 · Lesson 3   Two-Variable Sorting

---

variables and the corresponding values on the *Two-Variable Sorting* Activity Page. After collaborating with his or her partner about how they will organize the data, each student draws the tables. Some students will write the names of the groups for sorting each variable in separate tables. Others may want to display both variables in one table. Student pairs should analyze their data.

After students fill in their data tables, ask them to explain the purpose of their investigation, how they organized their data, and the results they see from the data. Discuss the pros and cons of each table, and ask students how they might change their tables if they did the investigation again.

One second grade class wanted to find if the most common color used for lids was the same for small, medium, and large lids. One student pair drew two boxes with which to size the lids. They decided that small-sized lids should fit inside a square that was 2 inches by 2 inches. If a lid was larger than that square, it would be placed inside a square that was 5 inches by 5 inches. If the lid fit inside that square, it was a medium-sized lid. If it was larger than that, then it was a large-sized lid. After planning their strategy, they decided how to organize their data. Figure 3 shows the table they created.

Small-size Lids		Medium-size Lids		Large-size Lids	
C Color	**N** Number	**C** Color	**N** Number	**C** Color	**N** Number
white	7	white	2	white	1
silver	5	silver	4	silver	0
gold	8	gold	2	gold	0
black	4	black	1	black	0
other	9	other	6	other	1

Figure 3: *One student pair started with three tables when sorting by size and color*

When the student pair presented their investigation, their classmates suggested that the colors didn't have to be written three times since the color values were the same for all three sizes. Figure 4 shows the table the class thought the pair could use if the investigation was repeated.

Sorting Lids Data Table

C Color	S Size		
	Small	Medium	Large
white	7	2	1
silver	5	4	0
gold	8	2	0
black	4	1	0
other	9	6	1

Figure 4: *The class's revision*

Encourage students to revise their data tables. Discuss how the revisions may have made the data easier to read and compare.

Suggestions for Teaching the Lesson

Math Facts

DPP item G provides practice with the subtraction facts for Group C in the context of money.

Homework and Practice

- The *Keenya and Michael's Lids* Homework Pages ask students to analyze data from a two-variable sort.

- DPP item H builds number sense and estimation skills. Items I and J provide computation practice. Item I practices division and item J asks for more than one way to solve two-digit addition and subtraction problems.

Assessment

- Listening to students' explanations and their classmates' suggestions will provide insight into each student's level of understanding. Observe students' two-variable sorting process and their organization skills for recording data. Record your observations on the *Observational Assessment Record.*

- The *Frank and Kaley's Lids* Assessment Pages allow you to assess students' abilities to interpret data and draw conclusions. This assessment can be done in pairs or small groups.

Name _____ Date _____

Frank and Kaley's Lids

Frank and Kaley chose to study the material and color of their lids. They made two data tables.

Lid Material

M Material	N Number
plastic	57
metal	33

Lid Color

C Color	N Number
white	11
red	5
blue	23
silver	17
gold	24
other	10

Use the tables to answer the questions.

1. What is the most common color? _____

Two-Variable Sorting   SG · Grade 2 · Unit 13 · Lesson 3 355

Student Guide - Page 355

Name _____ Date _____

2. How many lids are there altogether? How did you find your answer? _____

3. What is another way to find out how many lids there are? _____

4. Can you tell how many of the plastic lids are red?
   Explain. _____

Discuss

Frank and Kaley want to compare the color of metal lids and plastic lids. Discuss with your partner or group some other ways that Frank and Kaley can make data tables for their study. Show your new data tables below.

356 SG · Grade 2 · Unit 13 · Lesson 3   Two-Variable Sorting

Student Guide - Page 356

AT A GLANCE

Math Facts and Daily Practice and Problems

DPP item G provides practice with subtraction facts. Item H builds number sense. Items I and J are computation practice.

Developing the Activity (A1) (A2) (A3) (A5)

1. Tell students that they will study two variables at once just as Professor Robinson and Betty did in the *Monkey Business* Adventure Book story.
2. Discuss possible questions to answer when studying two variables with lids.
3. The whole class agrees on a question to study.
4. Students write the purpose and draw a picture on the *Two-Variable Sorting* Activity Pages.
5. Pairs collaborate on how they will organize the data.
6. Each student prepares his or her own data table on the *Two-Variable Sorting* Activity Pages.
7. Using a sample of 20–30 lids, students collect, record, and analyze their data.
8. The class discusses the investigation.

Homework

Assign the *Keenya and Michael's Lids* Homework Pages.

Assessment

1. Students complete the *Frank and Kaley's Lids* Assessment Pages.
2. Use Assessment Indicator (A5) and the *Observational Assessment Record* to note students' understanding of a two-variable sort.

Notes:

Student Guide

Two-Variable Sorting (SG pp. 351–352)

Answers and pictures will vary.

Keenya and Michael's Lids (SG pp. 353–354)

Questions 1–5

1. more large lids in all (29 + 8 = 37 large lids)
2. medium lids
3. large lids
4. There are the same number of metal and plastic lids.
5. Answers will vary. Two possible ways are shown.

M Material	S Size		
	small	medium	large
metal	7	5	29
plastic	3	30	8

S Size	M Number of metal lids	P Number of plastic lids
small	7	3
medium	5	30
large	29	8

Frank and Kaley's Lids (SG pp. 355–356)

Questions 1–4

1. gold
2. 90 lids; Solution strategies will vary. One possible strategy is to add 57 and 33 together.
3. Solution strategies will vary. One possible strategy is to add: 11 + 5 + 23 + 17 + 24 + 10 = 90.
4. No, you can tell how many of the lids are plastic and how many of the lids are red, but not how many are plastic and red.

Answers will vary for data tables but one possibility is shown:

Plastic Lids

C Color	N Number
white	
red	
blue	
silver	
gold	
other	

Metal Lids

C Color	N Number
white	
red	
blue	
silver	
gold	
other	

*Answers and/or discussion are included in the Lesson Guide.

Daily Practice and Problems

K. Subtraction with Tens and Hundreds (URG p. 11)

1. 7 − 4 = __

2. 70 − 40 = __

3. 700 − 400 = __

4. __ = 11 − 6

5. __ = 110 − 60

6. __ = 1100 − 600

L. Time (URG p. 12)

It is 4:30.

1. Franco came home from band practice a half hour ago. What time did he come home?

2. In one hour he will set the dinner table. At what time will he set the table?

3. In four hours he will go to bed. At what time will Franco go to bed?

M. Number Sense (URG p. 12)

87 + 29

1. Is the answer less than 50?

2. Is the answer between 50 and 100?

3. Is the answer more than 100?

4. Is the answer closer to 100 or 125?

N. Word Problems (URG p. 12)

A. Sol made 11 valentines and gave 6 to his friends. He gave the rest of the cards to his cousins. How many valentines did Sol give to his cousins?

B. Tess had 12 candy hearts. Sandy had 5 fewer hearts than Tess. How many candy hearts did Sandy have?

Undercover Investigation

Estimated Class Sessions: 3

This class investigation involves a two-variable sort with lids. The class chooses which variables and values to study, student pairs carry out the lab, and data is combined into a class data table and graph. Students may discover that the data collected from a large sample—the class—produces different results than the data collected from a small sample—an individual student pair.

Key Content

- Sorting a collection of objects by two variables.
- Collecting, organizing, graphing, and analyzing data.
- Making predictions based on a sample.
- Comparing results from a small and large sample.
- Making and interpreting bar graphs.

Key Vocabulary

sample

O. Subtraction Facts Quiz: Group C (URG p. 13)

A. 6 − 3 = __   B. 9 − 5 = __

C. 11 − 6 = __   D. __ = 7 − 3

E. 8 − 4 = __   F. __ = 12 − 7

G. 11 − 5 = __   H. 9 − 4 = __

I. 12 − 6 = __   J. 7 − 4 = __

K. __ = 10 − 5   L. 12 − 5 = __

Explain how you solved D.

P. Rocks (URG p. 13)

1. Marjorie measured the volume of a rock. She filled a graduated cylinder to 40 cc. After she placed the rock inside, the water rose to 48 cc. What is the volume of her rock?

2. If Marjorie's rock had a twin and she placed it inside the cylinder too, to what level would the water rise?

Suggestions for using the DPPs are on page 39.

Curriculum Sequence

Before This Unit

In Unit 3 of second grade, students sorted a collection of buttons by different variables and used the TIMS Laboratory Method to organize, graph, and analyze their results.

After This Unit

In Unit 1 of third grade, students will analyze a sample from a population, using the TIMS Laboratory Method.

Materials List

Print Materials for Students

		Math Facts and Daily Practice and Problems	Lab	Homework	Written Assessment
Student Book	**Student Guide**		*Undercover Investigation* Pages 357–358	*Megan and Danny's Lids* Page 359	*Mena Sorts for Recycling* Pages 361–362
Teacher Resources	**Facts Resource Guide**	DPP Items 13K, 13N & 13O			DPP Item 13O *Subtraction Facts Quiz: Group C*
	Unit Resource Guide	DPP Items K–P Pages 11–13			DPP Item O *Subtraction Facts Quiz: Group C* Page 13
	Generic Section		*Vertical Bar Graph,* 2 per student		

available on Teacher Resource CD

All Transparency Masters, Blackline Masters, and Assessment Blackline Masters in the Unit Resource Guide are on the Teacher Resource CD.

Supplies for Each Student Pair

20–30 lids

Materials for the Teacher

Observational Assessment Record (Unit Resource Guide, Pages 5–6 and Teacher Resource CD)
Individual Assessment Record Sheet (Teacher Implementation Guide, Assessment Section and Teacher Resource CD)
2 transparencies of *Vertical Bar Graph,* optional
class data table
2 class graphs

POSSIBLE VARIABLES AND THEIR VALUES

Variables	Names of Groups (Values)
material	plastic, metal
size	small, medium, large

Figure 5: *Variables and values chosen by a TIMS class*

Before the Lab

Consolidate all the lids into one large collection.

Developing the Lab

Part 1. Setting Up the Investigation

Explain to the class that they will conduct an investigation in a similar manner as Professor Robinson and Betty did in the *Monkey Business* Adventure Book. Ask:

*   *What questions can we ask about the lids that people throw away?*

The questions that students have about lids will probably be the same as those they shared in Lesson 3 *Two-Variable Sorting.* Display a list of those questions on an overhead transparency and add any new questions to the list. Questions may include:

*   *Do plastic lids weigh more than metal lids?*
*   *Are plastic lids made in different sizes than metal lids?*
*   *Is the size of a lid related to its color?*

Guide the class to agree on one question to investigate. Encourage them to identify the two variables and their groups for sorting (their corresponding values). One class decided to find out whether there is a connection between the size of a lid and the type of material used to make the lid. The table in Figure 5 lists the variables and values they agreed to study.

Tell students that data will first be collected by student pairs using their small collections (samples) of lids. Then all the data will be put together into the class data table. This table will include the data from all the lids in the class collection.

Ask the class to discuss possible data tables they can use to organize their own data and the class data. Emphasize that there are many good ways of organizing the data, but a common method of organization is necessary so that pairs can compare their results easily. Start preparing the class data table and label it according to the variables and values the students agree on.

Have students collaborate on how they will graph their data so they can display it clearly for analysis. Label the class graphs according to the variables and values the class will investigate.

Figures 6 and 7 show a class data table and graphs a classroom made for recording their data.

Undercover Investigation

M Material	S Size		
	Small	Medium	Large
plastic	178	96	61
metal	53	74	38

Figure 6: *A sample class table*

Part 2. Investigating a Sample

Have one student from each pair scoop up a number of lids from the consolidated lid collection, using both hands and with eyes closed. Tell students not to try to select particular lids but simply to use those lids that come in their two-handed scoop. Tell them that each pair's small group of lids is called a **sample** of the whole class collection of lids. A **sample** is what scientists call a small group taken out of a large collection. By measuring the sample, they can make predictions about the large collection or group. Discuss whether it is important to mix up the lids before scooping out a sample. One method of selecting samples is to prepare them in plastic bags ahead of time. If choosing this option, however, make sure that the students are aware that the individual samples were chosen randomly.

After introducing the *Undercover Investigation* Lab Pages, remind students to follow the TIMS Laboratory Method to conduct their investigation. In particular, students should:

1. Draw a picture of their investigation that includes the two variables and the groups for sorting each variable.

2. Draw the data tables the class has agreed to use. Sort the lids and record the results in the table.

3. Label the vertical and horizontal axes on a *Vertical Bar Graph* Generic Page and graph the results for both variables. Though the data for both variables can be graphed on a single graph, we recommend at this point that separate graphs be made for each variable. To allow easy comparison of the data for the two variables, the vertical axis on both graphs should have the same scale.

4. Discuss the data as a class. Sample questions are provided later in this guide.

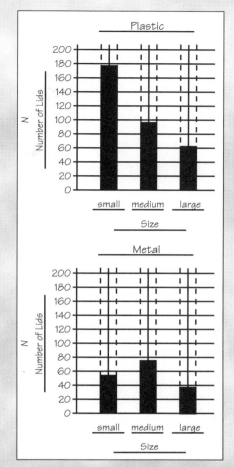

Figure 7: *A sample of two class graphs*

Name _____ Date _____

Undercover Investigation

Purpose: My class wants to find out _____

_____

Draw

Draw a picture. Show the two variables and the groups for sorting each variable. Write the names of the variables and the names of the groups.

Undercover Investigation SG · Grade 2 · Unit 13 · Lesson 4 357

Student Guide - Page 357

Name _____ Date _____

Co**ll**ect 🫙 ⠁⠂⠄

What data tables will you need? Draw the data tables your class decides to use. Sort your lids. Record the data.

Graph ⩗⩘

What bar graphs will you make? Decide with your class. Make your graphs on separate sheets of graph paper.

Discuss

1. What does your class data tell you about the lids that people usually throw away?

_____

_____

_____

_____

2. Compare your class results to the data you and your partner collected. Are the data similar?

_____

_____

_____

Student Guide - Page 358

Name _____ Date _____

Megan and Danny's Lids

Homework

Megan and Danny sorted a sample of lids and recorded their data.

Use the data to answer the questions.

Metal Lids		**Plastic Lids**	
S Size	**N** Number	**S** Size	**N** Number
small	𝍷𝍷𝍷 𝍷𝍷𝍷 || 12	small	𝍷𝍷𝍷 |||| 9
medium	||| 3	medium	𝍷𝍷𝍷 5
large	𝍷𝍷𝍷 | 6	large	𝍷𝍷𝍷 || 7

1. How many small plastic lids are there? _____

2. How many metal lids are there? _____

3. How many lids are there altogether? _____

4. How many medium-size lids are there? _____

5. Which table has twice as many small lids as large lids?

_____

6. Predict the number of large plastic lids there might be if Megan and Danny's sample were doubled.

Student Guide - Page 359

Part 3. Investigating with the Class

Ask each pair of students to present their findings to the class. Keep track of students' results on the blackboard and determine the total number for each value. Record this number in the class data table. Discuss how to scale the axes on the class bar graphs. Ask:

- *Should we number the vertical axis by ones, fives, tens, or twenties?*

After the axes are scaled, ask volunteers to draw the bars to the appropriate heights to display the compiled class data.

Guide children in analyzing and discussing the class data and in comparing the class's results with those obtained by pairs of students. The variables and values chosen by your class will determine the questions you will ask. Ask student pairs to summarize the class results. Encourage them to use phrases such as *most common* or *least common* and *most likely* or *least likely* when applicable.

After analyzing the class data, compare the results to those obtained by each student pair. Ask questions concerning the overall shapes of the bar graphs. You may find that although some pairs had different results than the class, the majority of the pairs obtained results similar to the class's data. The following questions can assist with the analysis. Modify the questions to fit the variables and values chosen by the class.

1. *What is the most common (size) for (plastic lids)?*

2. *What is the least common (size) for (plastic lids)?*

3. *How many lids do we have of each (size)?*

4. *How many more (small lids) do we have than (large lids)?*

5. *Do we have twice as many (small lids) as (large lids)?*

6. *What is the total number of lids in our sample?*

7. *What does our class data show us about the lids people usually throw away?*

8. *Are our class's results similar to your pair's results?*

9. *How do you think the number of lids in a sample affects the results? (The larger the sample, the more it will reflect the data for the whole collection.)*

10. *How might the results be different if we studied samples of lids from our entire state? from across the United States? from each continent?*

11. *Would you expect the numbers to be different? How? Why?*

12. *Would you expect the shape of the graphs to look different? How? Why?*

Ask students to complete the questions on their *Undercover Investigation* Lab Pages.

Suggestions for Teaching the Lesson

Math Facts

DPP item K builds number sense and computation skill by providing subtraction facts practice using multiples of ten and one hundred. Item N contains two word problems that use subtraction facts.

Homework and Practice

- The *Megan and Danny's Lids* Homework Page provides practice in reading a table and in predicting numbers for a larger sample.

- DPP item L provides practice with time. Item M builds number sense and estimation skills. Item P provides computation practice in the context of measuring volume using a graduated cylinder.

Assessment

- Use the *Mena Sorts for Recycling* Assessment Pages to assess students' abilities to read and interpret tables.

- Use DPP item O *Subtraction Facts Quiz: Group C,* Assessment Indicator (A7), and the *Observational Assessment Record* to document students' progress with the subtraction facts for Group C.

- Transfer appropriate assessment documentation from the Unit 13 *Observational Assessment Record* to students' *Individual Assessment Record Sheets*.

Extension

Students can sort the lids again looking at other variables.

Name _____ Date _____

Mena Sorts for Recycling

Mena collects lids to be recycled. She sorts them by color and material. Here is the data table she made for this week. Use her data to answer the questions.

M Material	C Color		
	Gold	Black	White
metal	7	2	3
plastic	14	7	20

1. A. Are there more black lids or white lids?

   _____

   B. How many more?

   _____

2. A. Are there more gold lids or white lids?

   _____

   B. How many more?

   _____

Undercover Investigation   SG · Grade 2 · Unit 13 · Lesson 4 361

Student Guide - Page 361

Name _____ Date _____

3. Which color has the greatest number of lids?

   _____

4. Which color has the fewest number of lids?

   _____

5. A. Are there more plastic lids or metal lids?

   _____

   B. How many more?

   _____

   C. Is it more than twice as many more?

   _____

6. Mena collected twice as many lids last week. Estimate the number of plastic lids that she collected last week. Explain how you got that number.

   _____

   _____

   _____

   _____

362 SG · Grade 2 · Unit 13 · Lesson 4   Undercover Investigation

Student Guide - Page 362

Math Facts and Daily Practice and Problems (A7)

DPP items K and N provide practice with the subtraction facts. Item O is a short quiz on the subtraction facts for Group C. Item L involves telling time. Item M builds number sense and item P builds computation skills.

Part 1. Setting Up the Investigation (A1) (A3) (A5)

1. Ask, *"In what ways can we sort our collection of lids?"*
2. Display the list of questions students generated in Lesson 3 *Two-Variable Sorting*. Add new questions to the list.
3. Agree on the question to investigate. Identify the two variables and their corresponding values.
4. Discuss possible ways to draw a data table. Label the class data table.
5. Students collaborate on how they will graph their data.
6. Label the class graph according to the variables and values the class will investigate.

Part 2. Investigating a Sample (A1) (A2) (A3) (A4) (A5)

1. Each student pair takes a sample from the lid collection.
2. Students draw a picture of their investigation on the *Undercover Investigation* Lab Pages.
3. Student pairs sort the lids and record the results on a data table.
4. Student pairs label the vertical and horizontal axes on *Vertical Bar Graph* Generic Pages and graph their data.
5. Discuss the data as a class.

Part 3. Investigating with the Class (A3) (A4) (A6)

1. Partners share their findings with the class and record their data on the class table.
2. Find the total number for each value in the class data table.
3. Scale the axes on the class bar graph appropriately.
4. Student volunteers draw the bars to the appropriate heights to display the compiled class data.
5. Students analyze the class data and compare it to results obtained by pairs of students.
6. Students complete *Questions 1–2* on the *Undercover Investigation* Lab Pages.

Homework

Assign the *Megan and Danny's Lids* Homework Page.

Assessment

1. Students complete the *Mena Sorts for Recycling* Assessment Pages.
2. Use DPP item O, Assessment Indicator (A7), and the *Observational Assessment Record* to document students' fluency with the subtraction facts for Group C.
3. Transfer appropriate documentation from the Unit 13 *Observational Assessment Record* to the students' *Individual Assessment Record Sheets*.

Notes:

Student Guide

Undercover Investigation (SG pp. 357–358)

Questions 1–2

Answers and drawings will vary.

*See Figure 6 in Lesson Guide 4 for a sample data table.

*See Figure 7 in Lesson Guide for sample graphs.

1.–2. Answers will vary.

Megan and Danny's Lids (SG p. 359)

Questions 1–6

1. 9 lids
2. 21 lids
3. 42 lids
4. 8 lids
5. metal lids table
6. Predictions will vary; 14 lids is a good prediction.

Mena Sorts for Recycling (SG pp. 361–362)

Questions 1–6

1. **A.** white
   B. 14 lids
2. **A.** white lids
   B. 2 lids
3. white lids
4. black lids
5. **A.** plastic lids
   B. 29 lids
   C. yes
6. Estimates will vary. 80–85 plastic lids is a good estimate. Solution strategies will vary. One possible strategy is to estimate the number of plastic lids she collected the first week, then double the estimate.

*Answers and/or discussion are included in the Lesson Guide.